WIN THE HEART

HOW TO CREATE A CULTURE OF FULL ENGAGEMENT

FIELD GUIDE

MARK MILLER & RANDY GRAVITT

Printed in the United States of America
Design and Layout by Lindsay Miller
Research Contributions by Rebekah Kerr & Scott Morgan

Printing Information
Bennett Graphics
125 Royal Woods Court, Suite 100
Tucker, GA 30084

ISBN 978-0-9998210-6-0

CONTENTS

The life of a leader can be hectic. On most days, we have a dizzying array of problems screaming for our attention—internal pressures such as staffing, quality, and capacity issues combined with external storm clouds propelling the war for talent, competitive pressures, and ever-changing governmental regulations, to name just a few. In the midst of this cacophony is brewing a threat to our organizations, often unseen and unheard above the daily din—the thief of sales, profits, customer satisfaction, and the pride in a job well done: low employee engagement.

The data on this topic is so consistently shocking, most leaders have become numb to the annual statistics. Some have even retreated into denial and chosen to stop thinking and talking about engagement. This is not the answer. Engagement matters for several reasons.

First, there are the people. Their work life matters. As leaders, we have an opportunity to help people find meaning and purpose in their work. We can create a place where they can bring their best selves to work every day. The workplace we create determines, to a large extent, how engaged someone is at work. Do your people go home energized or disempowered at the end of a long day? We really do have the responsibility to decide.

Leaders should also care deeply about engagement because of the opportunity it presents. If we can harness the untapped potential buried deep within the hearts of our people, we can turn engagement from a liability into a real, sustainable, competitive advantage and usher in gains in productivity unseen since the industrial revolution!

For many organizations, engagement is the final hurdle to becoming a High Performance Organization. This journey is outlined in *Chess Not Checkers.* (See pp 118-123 for more resources.) For those who are not familiar with the concepts, here is a ten-second summary: All High Performance Organizations have four things in common. They Bet on Leadership (*Leaders Made Here*), Act as One (*Talent Magnet*), and Win the Heart (covered in the book and this field guide). These three "moves" enable them to Excel at Execution (to be covered in a book to be released in the spring of 2020).

Here's our encouragement to you: keep an open mind, check your assumptions about engagement at the door, and get ready to unleash the full potential of your people and your organization.

Mark and Randy

HOW TO USE THIS FIELD GUIDE

On the following pages, you will find a deep dive on each of the cornerstones of engagement: assessment questions, examples from successful organizations, ideas for action, team meeting templates, and more. Pick and choose the activities that will serve you and your team. Customize them as you see fit and share them widely, but most importantly, put the ideas into action and change your organization for the better.

BURIED TREAS

THE GOAL

As already referenced, there is a lot of information in the world on Engagement—the elusive elixir every leader is searching for. Like Ponce de Leon's Fountain of Youth, the keys to engagement would allow your organization to live, profitably, forever.

You can stop your search. **WIN THE HEART** will remove the cloak of mystery and uncertainty around engagement.

The path forward begins with a simple definition.

ENGAGEMENT = LEVEL OF CARE.

That's it. If someone cares, they are highly engaged. This shows up in energy, effort, creativity, and profitability. If someone doesn't care very much, the consequences are equally recognizable: apathy, lethargy, and indifference, for starters.

So, how do you create an organization full of these caring, fully-engaged employees? In the book, **WIN THE HEART**, and in this Field Guide, we outline the four cornerstones on which you can build a place where people really care about their customers, co-workers, and the organization.

Connection

Affirmation

Responsibility

Environment

So, in the final analysis, **CARE** produces caring!

Do you know where to find the world's greatest reservoir of natural resources?

Your mind may immediately go to the oil fields of the Middle East or the diamond mines of South Africa, or maybe, you think about the vast reserves of gold and natural gas yet to be unearthed in Alaska. If you thought any of these, you would be incorrect.

The greatest untapped resource in the world resides within the four walls of businesses around the globe—the virtually unlimited supply of passion, energy, and creativity resident in the hearts and minds of your employees.

In recent years, much has been discussed and written about the malaise which has overtaken the workplace. As mentioned in the introduction, some studies indicate as many as 70% of your workers are not fully engaged at work!

Let's assume for a moment this number is overstated. What if half your people really don't care about their work. What? Seriously? That would still be staggering and the implications: incalculable.

What this would mean in real terms—your grand vision would be dead on arrival. How many teams would win if only half the players care enough to run the plays? Well, the only way this works at all is if the other team is suffering from the same malady. Then, at least you are both playing at a comparable level of mediocrity.

What is the real problem here? Why has so much been written on this topic with so little effect? Make no mistake, the problem is real, but the diagnosis, in most cases, has been wrong. This chronic condition is not a problem with the workforce but with leadership.

That's where the book, **WIN THE HEART**, and this Field Guide come into play. These resources have been created for leaders. In them, you'll find the strategies and tactics you need to transform your organization.

CONNE

SECTION ONE

Why do some people care more than others? The answer is quite simple. **CONNECTION**. When people are connected to a person or cause, their level of care escalates and so does their engagement. As a leader, your responsibility is to keep people connected to what matters most.

The place to start is to remind your people how important your customers are—they actually determine whether your business stays in business or not. When employees understand your customers are really the key to your success and make an effort to add value to everyone who walks through the doors, the level of care changes. In turn, customers will care more about your products and services.

In highly engaged workplaces, there is care on both sides of the counter. Team Members are not only connected to the customers, they are also connected to each other. Serving alongside someone who truly cares about you as an individual, not just as an employee, is much easier. Good leaders constantly look for ways to create a culture of connection and community among the team.

Finally, the best leaders keep their people personally connected to the vision. They are able to connect the dots for people, reminding them often what they do and how they do it matters and that their work leads to meaningful impact.

Do you wish your people cared more? If so, you can accelerate engagement levels by encouraging connection to customers, to each other, and to your cause. When people are connected, engagement skyrockets!

When people are connected
CARE skyrockets!

BEST PRACTICES

CELEBRATE CUSTOMERS • CREATE BELONGING • PERSONALIZE VISION

CASE STUDY

The well-known online retail shop, Zappos, is going the extra mile to prove to employees and customers alike, they are important. By making personal connections with their customers, Zappos is known for their star customer service. For example, when someone visits their headquarters, they can expect to be personally greeted at the front desk and given a free bottle of water and popcorn (not to mention complimentary drinks/snacks throughout the tour and a free book at the end).

More impressive than the freebies, Zappos is noteworthy because of one of their values: “Build open and honest relationships with communication.” Employees have been recognized for sending flowers to customers or telling customers to donate incorrect orders to charity while the correct shoes are overnighted. Customer service agents are allowed to be just that—one agent spent 10 hours, 29 minutes just talking with a lonely customer. Zappos employees send out an estimated 50,000 thank you notes a year.

Customers are not the only beneficiary of connectivity at Zappos. The company has put a fresh twist on the commonplace tradition of awarding bonuses. Zappos started a “coworker bonus program” that allows employees to nominate and award a bonus of $50 each month to any specific coworker who went the extra mile for them or their team.

THE RESULTS

Because of their success through cultivating relationships, in 2009, Zappos was ranked 23rd in Fortune magazine's list of "100 Best Companies to Work For." They climbed to 15th in 2010, and again moved up to 6th in 2011. ***Zappos was also chosen as the Gold Stevie Winner of the Customer Service Department of the Year in 2018.***

BEST PRACTICE

CELEBR CUSTO

What matters most in your business? I hope your first thought is "our customers." Do you and your employees **CELEBRATE CUSTOMERS**? Truthfully, without customers, you are out of business.

Think back to a time when you had a horrible customer experience – a time when you were mistreated, ignored, or forced to wait unnecessarily. Most likely you decided not to go back, and you told your friends. Now put yourself in the shoes of one of your customers. Do people who visit your business feel important? Do they feel celebrated? If so, they become walking billboards for your products and services—happy customers are better than any marketing strategy you will ever have.

The great thing is when customers feel celebrated, it creates energy and engagement throughout your business. If you have the right people on your payroll, they will feel more valuable when they turn their focus to adding value to others.

Celebration begins with connection. Making eye contact, sharing a smile, learning a person's name, listening to their story, and responding to their feedback are all ways to communicate value. Does your team believe they are there to serve your customers or that the customers are there to serve them?

As the leader, you are responsible for reminding your people that customers should be celebrated not tolerated. If you truly want to create an environment where customers care about what you have to say or sell, then create a customer-centric business.

Customers should be celebrated, not tolerated.

SPOTLIGHT

HYATT

Hyatt's choice to focus on empathy over perfection put them on an unconventional path toward success in the hospitality industry. Instead of using a script when speaking to guests, Hyatt staff members are encouraged to be themselves during guest interactions. This creates a more authentic customer experience and encourages employees to establish an emotional connection with guests.

ASSESSMENT

RATE EACH STATEMENT USING THE FOLLOWING:

5	Strongly Agree	**2**	Disagree
4	Agree	**1**	Strongly Disagree
3	Neutral		

Our employees make eye contact, share a smile, and speak to our customers with warmth and appreciation. ________

Customer concerns are always addressed immediately and enthusiastically. ________

Every person on our team strives to exceed customer expectations. ________

Our employees view our customers as critical to our success. ________

We know our repeat customers by name and take time to know them personally. ________

Note any statements you ranked in the one to three range. How can you improve these areas? Consider Things You Can Do (p. 18) to address these development opportunities.

Happy customers are the best marketing strategy.

TEAM TIME

REVIEW WITH YOUR TEAM:

Dedicate 10-15 minutes of your next Team Meeting to work through two to three of the following questions and activities.

THINGS TO REMEMBER

1. **PEOPLE MATTER MORE THAN PROFITS**
2. **IN GREAT BUSINESSES, CUSTOMERS ARE CELEBRATED NOT TOLERATED**
3. **SATISFIED CUSTOMERS ARE BILLBOARDS FOR YOUR BUSINESS**

INTRODUCTION: Review the **BEST PRACTICE SPOTLIGHT: HYATT** (p. 15) and share the story with your team. What are their initial reactions? How could the leaders in your organization celebrate customers in a similar way?

ASSESSMENT: Take a minute to work through the assessment questions (p. 16) and discuss your answers with your team.

DISCUSSION: Where have you recently observed an employee in your organization celebrate a customer, and what effect did it have? How can you create more moments like this?

GROUP ACTIVITY: Review the **CELEBRATE CUSTOMERS THINGS YOU CAN DO** (p. 18) with the team, break into groups of three to four, and brainstorm additional ideas—challenge each group to develop at least ten more ideas and be prepared to report back to the team.

NEXT STEPS: Have each member of the team choose one of the ideas from the list on page 18 (or from the ideas generated during your group activity) and do it over the next week. Ask leaders to report back to the team at your next meeting.

THINGS YOU CAN DO

		DATE COMPLETED:
☐	**ATTITUDE OF GRATITUDE** Choose one customer weekly and celebrate them with a handwritten note from your team along with a gift card to a local ice cream or coffee shop.	
☐	**GET TO KNOW THE "REGULARS"** Challenge yourself and your team to learn the names of at least two regular customers every week.	
☐	**SECOND MILE SERVICE** Conduct a quarterly meeting with your leadership team to brainstorm ways you can go the "extra mile" for your customers.	
☐	**ABOVE AND BEYOND** Every month, ask your team to offer their input on how you can go "above and beyond" with your customer care.	
☐	**SAY THANKS** In every verbal interaction with your customers, ensure you and your team say thank you.	
☐	**CUSTOMER SPOTLIGHT** Create a monthly customer spotlight and express gratitude for their loyalty to your company.	
☐	**CUSTOMER ID** For your regular customers, create photo profiles with names and birthdays to share with your team. Any time they come into your business, greet them by name!	
☐	**DO UNTO OTHERS** Post the quote, "Do Unto Others," in a visible area for your team. Use it as a reminder to always treat others in the manner you want to be treated.	
☐	**SURPRISE AND DELIGHT** Empower your Team Members to offer customers a free sample or upgrade on your product or service from time to time to show your appreciation for the customer's business.	
☐	**WHY & WOW** Share the WHY (you exist) with your team daily and remind them to create WOW experiences for your customers.	

What else could you and other leaders do to **CELEBRATE CUSTOMERS**?

☐		
☐		

NOTES

BEST PRACTICE

CREATE BELONG

People crave belonging. From an early age, they seek out a group, clique, club, or team. While the desire to fit in is universal, without the right environment, connection can be difficult. Wise leaders understand community is cumulative over time, and they work hard to **CREATE BELONGING**.

The term "work family" has become popular for a reason. Many people feel the greatest sense of belonging when they are on the job. When leaders make everyone feel welcome, embrace diversity, and promote togetherness, the result is a depth of community that brings people together and accelerates performance.

Do your employees feel a sense of belonging, and do they value their coworkers as people, not just fellow employees. Engagement goes way up when people care about each other. You can accelerate this when you set the expectation and foster the environment for teamwork, and then set the pace by thinking and modeling we, not me.

Growing organizations are not built by leaders who merely clock in but by leaders who care. You cannot expect your employees to care 100% of the time unless you do. If you want to raise the level of engagement throughout your organization, care for your people and help them connect to each other. A place to belong is a powerful motivator for high performance.

Community is cumulative over time.

SPOTLIGHT

TWITTER

At Twitter, employees can't stop talking about how they love working with other smart people. Workers rave about belonging to a company that values human connectivity and love doing something that matters in the world. Employees say no one leaves until the work gets done.

ASSESSMENT

RATE EACH STATEMENT USING THE FOLLOWING:

5 Strongly Agree
4 Agree
3 Neutral
2 Disagree
1 Strongly Disagree

There is a genuine sense of belonging throughout our organization. __________

Our employees care for each other outside of work. __________

Our Team Members consistently on projects. __________

Senior members of the team work to include new Team Members and help them feel like a part of the group. __________

Diverse thinking and experience is welcomed and embraced at all levels of our business. __________

Note any statements you ranked in the one to three range. How can you improve these areas? Consider Things You Can Do (p. 24) to address these development opportunities.

A place to belong is a powerful motivator for high performance.

TEAM TIME

REVIEW WITH YOUR TEAM:

Dedicate 10-15 minutes of your next Team Meeting to work through two to three of the following questions and activities.

THINGS TO REMEMBER

1. **THE DESIRE TO FIT INTO A GROUP IS UNIVERSAL**
2. **LEADERS ARE RESPONSIBLE FOR MODELING CARE & CREATING CONNECTION**
3. **A PLACE TO BELONG IS A POWERFUL MOTIVATOR FOR HIGH PERFORMANCE**

INTRODUCTION: Review the **BEST PRACTICE SPOTLIGHT: TWITTER** (p. 21) and share the story with your team. What are their initial reactions? How could your organization create similar connections?

ASSESSMENT: Take a minute to work through the assessment questions (p. 22) and debrief your answers with your team.

DISCUSSION: Where have you recently observed a leader in our organization help a Team Member feel connected to the group, and what effect did it have? How can we recreate more connections like this?

GROUP ACTIVITY: Review the **CREATE BELONGING THINGS YOU CAN DO** (p. 24) with the team, break into groups of three to four, and brainstorm additional ideas—challenge each group to develop at least ten more ideas and be prepared to report back to the team.

NEXT STEPS: Have each member of the team choose one of the ideas from the list on page 24 (or from the ideas generated during your group activity) and do it over the next week. Ask leaders to report back to the team at your next meeting.

THINGS YOU CAN DO

		DATE COMPLETED:
☐	**STORY TIME** Knowing is the first step in building genuine community. At an upcoming meeting or retreat, ask the attendees to share their personal story.	
☐	**RANDOM ACTS OF KINDNESS** This week, find several opportunities to do something nice for members of your team – for no reason at all.	
☐	**NEW TEAM MEMBER MEAL** Schedule a meal out with all new Team Members, paid for by the organization.	
☐	**CHILI COOK OFF** Invite employees and their families to participate in an annual chili cook off. Provide prizes to the winners.	
☐	**JUST A NOTE** Try an old-school idea: write a personal note with a pen and paper to a co-worker expressing thanks, congratulations, or appreciation. Do this once a week for the next four weeks and check the response.	
☐	**BUDGET FOR BELONGING** As you set your budget for next year, be sure to include a line item to fund employee connection activities.	
☐	**HOME DELIVERY** Order a meal for a coworker who is out with an illness. To take it to the next level, create a hospitality team in your company who makes homemade meals for people in need!	
☐	**ORGANIC GATHERINGS** Have impromptu gatherings as often as possible and invite every member of your team to join the fun.	
☐	**E-CONNECT** Establish a social media presence for your team and update with photos, birthdays, anniversaries, and other information that will encourage the team!	
☐	**GLAD TO KNOW YOU** Every day, try to learn something about the personal life of a fellow Team Member. Do this for 30 days and see how it transforms your culture.	

What else could you and other leaders do to **CREATE BELONGING**?

☐		
☐		

NOTES

BEST PRACTICE

PERSO
VISION

Leaders not only see the future, they help others see it also. But it is one thing to cast vision and another to **PERSONALIZE VISION** for each employee. This can take on many forms. From creating role clarity to providing feedback, leaders convey they are interested in the success and future of their Team Members.

How do you help people care more? How do you raise their level of engagement? As a leader, your job is to make sure everyone feels connected to the work. If your team doesn't see value in the vision and understand how their individual work contributes to fulfilling it, they will never engage. The temptation can be to only cast vision broadly, but when leaders have real conversations with individuals, it becomes personal.

Are your people locked in on contributing to the vision? Have they personalized it to their specific role and responsibility? If not, maybe it is time for you to remind people why their work matters. If you and your leaders will take the time to personalize the vision for every employee, your people will care more, and engagement always energizes effort.

When people see their work as more than a job they bring their best to their role.

SPOTLIGHT

SOUTHWEST AIRLINES

In the airline industry, Southwest is known for connecting their people to what matters most. Southwest employees do not see themselves as mere transporters of passengers but as enablers who connect customers to people and places they love. This is a small differentiation but makes a big difference in how important an employee perceives his/her job.

ASSESSMENT

RATE EACH STATEMENT USING THE FOLLOWING:

5	Strongly Agree	**2**	Disagree
4	Agree	**1**	Strongly Disagree
3	Neutral		

Every person in our organization is crystal clear on the vision. ________

Our leaders have ongoing vision conversations with individuals and teams. ________

All of our employees understand how their role contributes to the vision. ________

Our people share the vision with others – inside and outside the organization. ________

Everyone consistently makes decisions in alignment with the vision. ________

Note any statements you ranked in the one to three range. How can you improve these areas? Consider Things You Can Do (p. 30) to address these development opportunities.

The best leaders keep individuals connected to the vision.

TEAM TIME

REVIEW WITH YOUR TEAM:

Dedicate 10-15 minutes of your next Team Meeting to work through two to three of the following questions and activities.

THINGS TO REMEMBER

1. **GREAT LEADERS CONSTANTLY PERSONALIZE THE VISION**
2. **REMIND PEOPLE OFTEN WHAT THEY DO MATTERS**
3. **PEOPLE IN HIGH PERFORMANCE ORGANIZATIONS EMBRACE THE VISION AT EVERY LEVEL**

INTRODUCTION: Review the **BEST PRACTICE SPOTLIGHT: SOUTHWEST AIRLINES** (p. 27) and share the story with your team. What are their initial reactions? How could you better connect people to the vision in your organization?

ASSESSMENT: Take a minute to work through the assessment questions (p. 28) and debrief your answers with your team.

DISCUSSION: Where have you recently observed a leader in our organization personalize the vision for a Team Member, and what effect did it have? How can we connect more people to the vision?

GROUP ACTIVITY: Review the **PERSONALIZE VISION THINGS YOU CAN DO** (p. 30) with the team, break into groups of three to four, and brainstorm additional ideas—challenge each group to develop at least ten more ideas and be prepared to report back to the team.

NEXT STEPS: Have each member of the team choose one of the ideas from the list on page 30 (or from the ideas generated during your group activity) and do it over the next week. Ask leaders to report back to the team at your next meeting.

THINGS YOU CAN DO

	DATE COMPLETED:
☐ **KNOW THE WHY** Create an easy to remember statement that explains why you exist as an organization and ensure everyone knows it.	
☐ **ASK THEM** During your one-on-one evaluations, make sure you ask Team Members what part they played in living out the vision of the company.	
☐ **LAST MONTH LOOKBACK** Ask each member of your team to identify the most important thing they did to live out the vision of the organization during the past month.	
☐ **POWER OF STORY** Your team needs to know the history of your organization. During orientation and at least twice a year moving forward, highlight the history of the company.	
☐ **PHOTO LINE UP** Give all new Team Members an organizational chart with names, photos, and positions of every leader in the organization.	
☐ **MAKE HEROES** Be on the lookout for examples of your Team Members living the vision. When you spot one, make a big deal out of it. The people living your vision every day are your heroes – recognize them.	
☐ **WHAT IS AND WHAT COULD BE** Spend ten minutes during every team meeting explaining where you are AND where you could be as an organization. Use this as motivation to dream big!	
☐ **IMPORTANCE OF OWNERSHIP** During all employee evaluations, explain the importance every Team Member plays in owning their area of responsibility.	
☐ **30 DAY CHECK UP** Every 30 days, ask every Team Member to share the vision of your company and why it is critical to your success.	
☐ **VISION DEMO** Every month, ask your leadership team what they are doing to share the company vision verbally and how they are demonstrating it with their actions.	

What else could you and other leaders do to **PERSONALIZE VISION**?

☐	
☐	

NOTES

CONNECTION SUMMARY

When people are connected to a person or a cause, their level of engagement is raised. As a leader, your responsibility is to keep your people connected to the customers, to each other, and to your vision.

BEST PRACTICES REVIEW

CELEBRATE CUSTOMERS – Constantly remind your team, "The customer who pays the bills and ensures our future success."

CREATE BELONGING – Foster an environment where your team connects to and serves one another.

PERSONALIZE VISION – Remind your people of why their work matters.

NEXT STEPS

- Do a Connection audit by reviewing the assessment questions on pages 16, 22, and 28 to evaluate whether the above best practices are present in your organization. Create a plan to close any gaps you discover, and challenge your team to share responsibility with everyone in the company.
- Have a monthly conversation with your leadership team and identify areas where each of you can increase your connections. Share stories of progress moving forward.
- Beginning immediately, set a personal goal of making a true connection with at least one customer and one Team Member every week. Additionally, have one conversation every week to remind an employee of why their work matters and how it connects to the overall vision.

NOTES

The one thing I need to do to increase **CONNECTION** is:

Other thoughts:

AFFIRM

SECTION TWO

Few things are as important as AFFIRMATION. If you can create a culture where appreciation is freely given and received, you will enjoy a staggering amount of energy, engagement, and good will. Leaders who understand this and work to make people feel valued create an engaged workforce that produces amazing results.

There are many ways to affirm those on your team. Perhaps the greatest is to appreciate people and their effort. A simple "thank you" goes a long way toward communicating you care about your people. When you see someone doing something great, say something.

In order to create a culture of affirmation, you also need to make sure everyone is included. Thank high performers but don't neglect those lagging behind. The best leaders understand that validation is not only about performance but about the individual. When you validate people for who they are in addition to what they do, performance often improves.

Finally, when leaders foster the dreams of their people, the message comes through loud and clear—"You matter to me as a human being!" When you understand your people carry with them hopes, dreams, and aspirations for a better life, and you help them realize these, increased engagement is virtually guaranteed.

Do you want your people to be more engaged? If so, don't allow them to wonder whether or not they matter. As the leader, you are the architect of the culture in your organization. Design a place where everyone receives affirmation, and your people will love coming to work.

Affirmation is the foundation of engagement.

BEST PRACTICES

SHOW APPRECIATION • • • **VALIDATE PEOPLE** • • • **FOSTER DREAMS**

CASE STUDY

At Red Velvet Events (RVE), employees used a small plastic troll named Pockets to celebrate each other. Crazy as it may sound, during their weekly staff meeting, a Red Velvet Team Member gave Pockets to a coworker and described the recipient's hard work throughout the past week. Each person who received the doll gave it another accessory (bracelet, tattoo, necktie, etc.) and presented it to another Team Member the following week.

Though a seemingly insignificant gesture, morale and engagement were boosted in the workplace, as employees were affirmed for their efforts by the people who saw it firsthand. Over the years, RVE used and retired six different beloved, accessorized versions of Pockets.

Recently, the company decided to freshen up their "attitude of gratitude" tradition and replaced the shout-out doll with a jean jacket that employees can sign and wear each time they receive it. This quirky tradition not only reflects the company's pro-affirmation culture but also ensures employees notice and speak up when their fellow coworkers are winning at work.

As a four-year service celebration, each employee gets a personalized bobble head!

THE RESULTS

All the camaraderie has helped RVE grow substantially in recent years. In the summer of 2018, Red Velvet Events won second place out of 51 small businesses in the Austin Business Journal's "Best Places to Work" review. ***In that same summer, two different Espirit Awards from the International Live Events Association were earned by RVE employees.***

BEST PRACTICE

SHOW APPRE

Plato once wrote, "What is honored in a country is cultivated there." In other words, if you affirm a behavior, it will be repeated. Do you **SHOW APPRECIATION**? Face it, without your team you would not be able to accomplish very much. But there is a difference in having appreciation and showing it to those you lead. Great leaders create an environment of affirmation by showing appreciation.

If your Team Members are struggling to stay engaged, they may not feel valued. Recognition for a job well done, celebration for anniversaries and milestones, and even a heartfelt thank you can communicate gratitude and inspire your people to stay engaged.

Few things crush morale more than a contribution going unnoticed. What is worse, though, is when it is noticed and not acknowledged. Unfortunately, when it comes to great work, too many leaders see it but fail to say anything. They fall into the trap of driving toward results and fail to recognize they are sabotaging their own efforts by holding back praise.

Good leaders are secure enough to share credit with those in the trenches with them, and they are constantly using their words and actions to breath life into their people. Do your team a favor and become a leader who values effort and demonstrates appreciation. Remember, appreciation paves the path to greater engagement.

Humble leaders are secure enough to share credit with those on the front line.

IATION

SPOTLIGHT

GROUPON

At Groupon, every work anniversary (or Grouponiversary) is celebrated. At a two-year anniversary, an employee is recognized by receiving a sporty, bright green Adidas track jacket, and a black track jacket is given at the five-year milestone. Employees receive star patches for each additional year at the company and often personalize their jackets with fun nicknames.

ASSESSMENT

RATE EACH STATEMENT USING THE FOLLOWING:

5	Strongly Agree	2	Disagree
4	Agree	1	Strongly Disagree
3	Neutral		

Leaders in our organization are quick to share credit with those responsible for results. ___________

People say thank you and acknowledge those who help them achieve their goals. ___________

Employees feel appreciated by their supervisors throughout our business. ___________

Gratitude is expressed frequently by everyone. ___________

Appreciation is in the DNA of our organization. ___________

Note any statements you ranked in the one to three range. How can you improve these areas? Consider Things You Can Do (p. 44) to address these development opportunities.

Good leaders are secure enough to share credit.

TEAM TIME

REVIEW WITH YOUR TEAM:

Dedicate 10-15 minutes of your next Team Meeting to work through two to three of the following questions and activities.

THINGS TO REMEMBER

1. **A CULTURE OF GRATITUDE BRINGS OUT THE BEST IN PEOPLE**
2. **SECURE LEADERS SHARE CREDIT**
3. **APPRECIATION PAVES THE PATH TO GREATER ENGAGEMENT**

INTRODUCTION: Review the **BEST PRACTICE SPOTLIGHT: GROUPON** (p. 41) and share the story with your team. What are their initial reactions? What could you learn from the culture?

ASSESSMENT: Take a minute to work through the assessment questions (p. 42) and debrief your answers with your team.

DISCUSSION: Who have you recently observed in our organization show appreciation toward a teammate, and what effect did it have? How can we create more appreciation within our organization?

GROUP ACTIVITY: Review the **SHOW APPRECIATION THINGS YOU CAN DO** (p. 44) with the team, break into groups of three to four, and brainstorm additional ideas—challenge each group to develop at least ten more ideas and be prepared to report back to the team.

NEXT STEPS: Have each member of the team choose one of the ideas from the list on page 44 (or from the ideas generated during your group activity) and do it over the next week. Ask leaders to report back to the team at your next meeting.

THINGS YOU CAN DO

		DATE COMPLETED:
☐	**APPRECIATION LANGUAGE** There are a variety of ways to communicate appreciation. Ask each person on your team to identify what makes them feel appreciated (i.e. words, gifts, notes, etc.), and begin showing individual appreciation.	
☐	**ASK YOUR STAFF** Ask your team if they feel appreciated by the company and why or why not. Really listen and work to show appreciation using what you learn from your conversations.	
☐	**WRITTEN WORDS** Make it a point to handwrite three cards every week expressing your appreciation for your employees.	
☐	**APPRECIATION WEEK** Schedule an employee appreciation week at least two times each year. Make each day of appreciation week a special event with a different theme.	
☐	**NOT ANOTHER NUMBER** Do one thing each week to make one member of your team feel like more than just another number.	
☐	**PASS IT ON** Do at least one thing every day to express appreciation for a Team Member and encourage them to pass it on.	
☐	**TEACH > CRITIQUE** Over the next three months, encourage your leaders to spend more time teaching than critiquing.	
☐	**COACH THEM TO CARE** Brainstorm with your leaders about how you can coach your employees to express care regularly for one another.	
☐	**SHARE PRAISE** Anytime you see a Team Member doing something right, praise them publicly!	
☐	**RANDOM ACTS OF KINDNESS** Make it a habit for you and your leaders to do nice things for people for no specific reason other than to say thanks (i.e. bring doughnuts for the team, give out movie tickets or gift cards, etc.)	

What else could you and other leaders do to **SHOW APPRECIATION**?

☐		
☐		

NOTES

BEST PRACTICE

VALIDAT
PEOPLE

"Do I have what it takes?" A question asked countless times by workers all over the world. How about your people? Do you think they ever wonder? They shouldn't. As a leader, one of your greatest opportunities for influence is to assure your people that they matter and not just as employees. High performance leaders **VALIDATE PEOPLE**, accepting responsibility for making sure every employee feels valued.

Think back to a time when you were validated by one of your leaders. They encouraged you to keep reaching, challenged you to grow, or spoke life into you. Their belief in you made a difference in your life. In the same way, you have the opportunity to make people on your team feel individually valued. Who needs you to really see them and acknowledge their effort? Who needs a challenge or a stretch assignment? Who needs a word of encouragement or a note of appreciation?

The mantle of leadership carries with it a megaphone. What you say and do communicates loudly just how important you believe your people are. Your people need to know they matter. If you truly want to win their hearts, don't wait, validate!

Validation leads to motivation.

SPOTLIGHT

PATAGONIA

Patagonia understands accommodating your employees' needs and passions is the best way to validate their contribution. Their policy is when the surf is up, we surf (yes, even during work hours). Patagonia founder, Yvon Chouinard, titled his memoir *Let My People Go Surfing*. At Patagonia, they believe employees are more productive when they work and play together.

ASSESSMENT

RATE EACH STATEMENT USING THE FOLLOWING:

5	Strongly Agree	2	Disagree
4	Agree	1	Strongly Disagree
3	Neutral		

Every employee in our organization feels validated by their supervisor. ___________

Our Team Members are treated like people, not employees. ___________

Employees in our company are validated for who they are, not what they do. ___________

People in our organization know each other's interests outside of work. ___________

Our leaders validate everyone, not just top performers. ___________

Note any statements you ranked in the one to three range. How can you improve these areas? Consider Things You Can Do (p. 50) to address these development opportunities.

The leader's words carry the most weight.

TEAM TIME

REVIEW WITH YOUR TEAM:

Dedicate 10-15 minutes of your next Team Meeting to work through two to three of the following questions and activities.

THINGS TO REMEMBER

1. **THE LEADER'S WORDS CARRY THE MOST WEIGHT**
2. **VALIDATION CREATES MOTIVATION**
3. **PEOPLE MUST FEEL VALUED BY THEIR LEADERS**

INTRODUCTION: Review the **BEST PRACTICE SPOTLIGHT: PATAGONIA** (p. 47) and share the story with your team. What are their initial reactions? How well do you validate people?

ASSESSMENT: Take a minute to work through the assessment questions (p. 48) and debrief your answers with your team.

DISCUSSION: Where have you recently observed a leader in our organization validate a Team Member, and what effect did it have? How could we ensure everyone in our organization feels validated?

GROUP ACTIVITY: Review the **VALIDATE EVERYONE THINGS YOU CAN DO** (p. 50) with the team, break into groups of three to four, and brainstorm additional ideas—challenge each group to develop at least ten additional ideas and be prepared to report back to the team.

NEXT STEPS: Have each member of the team choose one of the ideas from the list on page 50 (or from the ideas generated during your group activity) and do it over the next week. Ask leaders to report back to the team at your next meeting.

THINGS YOU CAN DO

		DATE COMPLETED:
☐	**TALK & LISTEN** Make it a habit in your conversations to really listen to what others have to say.	
☐	**RESULTS & RELATIONSHIPS** Don't fall into the trap of only focusing on results. The best leaders value BOTH results AND relationships. Ask those you work with to help you modify your behavior as needed to ensure you don't miss either.	
☐	**INVEST FOR GROWTH** Offer at least one opportunity per month for your Team Members to grow. (Think: podcast, article, book, blog, or seminar).	
☐	**ACKNOWLEDGE EFFORT** At every team meeting, publicly acknowledge individual efforts.	
☐	**GIFT CARDS** Purchase a stack of gift cards monthly, and as you catch someone doing something great, give them one.	
☐	**CELEBRATE** Identify three people you can celebrate for a job well done.	
☐	**ENCOURAGING WORDS** Hang a whiteboard or create a virtual whiteboard where Team Members can share encouraging words about one another.	
☐	**WHAT'S THE SCORE?** Make sure you are sharing regularly with your team how your company is winning.	
☐	**VALIDATE THE TEAM** On your next successful team project, take time to call out individual contributions and validate the group for working well together.	
☐	**WHAT THEY SAID** Always make it a habit to share customer compliments publicly with the entire team. This is one way to let them know whether they are winning or losing.	

What else could you and other leaders do to **VALIDATE PEOPLE**?

☐		
☐		

NOTES

BEST PRACTICE

FOSTER DREAM

What is your number one dream? You probably know it. But do you know the dreams of the people on your team? Fostering dreams is a fantastic way to affirm your people.

The people in your organization carry with them hopes and aspirations for a better tomorrow. For some, these aspirations are why they show up every day. Certainly, a dream can be a powerful motivator. Unfortunately, too many hopes are squelched through the everyday grind. When dreams die, so does engagement. As the leader, you have the opportunity to create a place where dreams come true.

One way you can **FOSTER DREAMS** is to talk about them. Questions can be the gateway to help someone see and articulate a preferred future—perhaps for the first time. "What are you dreaming about?" "What would you like to be true in your life in a decade that is not true today?"

Lock in on the things that are important to those you lead, and you will become more important to them. After all, who doesn't admire a leader who makes dreams come true?

Dreams come in all shapes and sizes.

SPOTLIGHT

NETFLIX

Leadership at the binge-watching phenomenon, Netflix, certainly makes it a priority to look after employees who have begun their journey in building a family. New parents can decide to take up to a whopping one year of paid maternity and paternity leave. Parents have the choice to return part-time or full-time after their leave and can take extra time off whenever they need it.

ASSESSMENT

RATE EACH STATEMENT USING THE FOLLOWING:

- 5 Strongly Agree
- 4 Agree
- 3 Neutral
- 2 Disagree
- 1 Strongly Disagree

All leaders are aware of the aspirations of their direct reports. ________

Every employee is encouraged to pursue their dreams. ________

Our leaders work to remove barriers that stand between individuals and their dreams. ________

Dream conversations occur frequently in our organization. ________

Our organization is a place where dreams come true. ________

Note any statements you ranked in the one to three range. How can you improve these areas? Consider Things You Can Do (p. 56) to address these development opportunities.

Leaders who really care encourage people to go after their dreams.

TEAM TIME

REVIEW WITH YOUR TEAM:

Dedicate 10-15 minutes of your next Team Meeting to work through two to three of the following questions and activities.

THINGS TO REMEMBER

1. **IN THE BEST ORGANIZATIONS, PEOPLE ARE ENCOURAGED TO DREAM**
2. **GREAT LEADERS CELEBRATE THE DREAMS OF THEIR PEOPLE**
3. **PEOPLE WANT TO WORK FOR LEADERS WHO HELP MAKE DREAMS COME TRUE**

INTRODUCTION: Review the **BEST PRACTICE SPOTLIGHT: NETFLIX** (p. 53) and share the story with your team. What are their initial reactions? How well do you foster the dreams of your people?

ASSESSMENT: Take a minute to work through the assessment questions (p. 54) and debrief your answers with your team.

DISCUSSION: Where have you recently observed a leader in our organization encourage the dreams of a teammate, and what effect did it have? How could we become an organization where dreams come true?

GROUP ACTIVITY: Review the **FOSTER DREAMS THINGS YOU CAN DO** (p. 56) with the team, break into groups of three to four, and brainstorm additional ideas—challenge each group to develop at least ten additional ideas and be prepared to report back to the team.

NEXT STEPS: Have each member of the team choose one of the ideas from the list on page 56 (or from the ideas generated during your group activity) and do it over the next week. Ask leaders to report back to the team at your next meeting.

THINGS YOU CAN DO

	DATE COMPLETED:
☐ **START SMALL - DREAM BIG** Encourage every Team Member to have a dream, no matter how small. Once they achieve something small, challenge them to dream big.	
☐ **DREAM TO DEVELOP** Ensure every Team Member has a development plan focused on what is and what could be. Remind them to keep their dream in mind as they plan.	
☐ **SCHOLARSHIP PROGRAM** If you have the financial margin, create a company scholarship program to assist employees in furthering their education.	
☐ **30 MINUTE WALK THRU** Spend 30 minutes a day for the next week walking around and talking to your employees about their dreams, goals, and aspirations.	
☐ **LEADERS GO FIRST** As you encourage people to share their dream(s) with you, be prepared to share your dream first. Courage and vulnerability are traits people love to see in their leaders.	
☐ **BREAKING BARRIERS** Talk with your Team Members about potential barriers between them and their dream. Together, look for ways you can help remove the barriers.	
☐ **SUPPORT THEIR STORY** Ask your employees what support they need in order to live out their ideal story. Look for tangible ways you can help.	
☐ **POWER HOUR** Build in one hour every month for your employees to dream while "on the clock." Encourage people to record their thoughts and debrief with their supervisor the following day.	
☐ **DAILY DREAMS** Every day for the next week, ask at least one Team Member what they dream about as it relates to their life and career.	
☐ **TEAM DREAMS** As the leader, ask your team what they dream about accomplishing over the next year and do what you can to help them.	

What else could you and other leaders do to **FOSTER DREAMS**?

☐	
☐	

NOTES

AFFIRMATION SUMMARY

An environment of affirmation contributes far more to creating an engaged workforce than most leaders can imagine. As the leader, you are the architect of the culture. Design a place where everyone is validated, and your people will love coming to work.

BEST PRACTICES REVIEW

SHOW APPRECIATION – A culture of gratitude brings out the best in people.

VALIDATE PEOPLE – People must feel valued by their leaders.

FOSTER DREAMS – Strive to make your organization a place where dreams come true.

NEXT STEPS

- Do an Affirmation audit by reviewing the assessment questions on pages 42, 48, and 54 to evaluate whether the above best practices are present in your organization. Create a plan to close any gaps you discover, and challenge your team to share responsibility with everyone in the company.
- Have a monthly conversation with your leadership team and identify areas where each of you can do a better job of affirming your employees. Share stories of progress moving forward.
- Beginning immediately, set a personal goal of affirming at least one Team Member every day by writing a note to express appreciation, encouraging someone verbally, or having a dream conversation with a coworker.

NOTES

The one thing I need to do to increase **AFFIRMATION** is:

Other thoughts:

RESPON

SECTION THREE

Do you want your people to care more? If so, give them more **RESPONSIBILITY**. The sign of a great leader is not just the ability to attract followers but also to help people grow. Sharing responsibility is one of the best things you can do to develop your people and increase their engagement. High Performance Organizations are filled with people who take ownership of their role with an understanding of how it contributes to the overall mission.

One way you can give real responsibility is to delegate decisions. High-level leaders make the most critical, strategic decisions and give others the opportunity to share the tension in areas where the stakes are lower. Allowing a young leader to make decisions is a powerful tool for their development.

Sharing ownership is another great way to teach your people responsibility. Everything in your business needs an owner, and every person needs to own something. As the leader, you do not want to own everything. Challenge your people to take ownership and their energy level will soar.

Once you empower your people with decisions and tasks, you need to establish accountability. Believe it or not, people care more when they know they are going to be held accountable. Think back to how many times you did your homework knowing your teacher would ask for it the next day. Accountability is a great motivator.

When Team Members accept responsibility, it is an indicator they are being well led. Give your people the opportunity to share the load and everyone will benefit!

SIBILITY

If you just hire a man's hands, you miss the opportunity to win his heart!

BEST PRACTICES

DELEGATE DECISIONS • SHARE OWNERSHIP • ESTABLISH ACCOUNTABILITY

CASE STUDY

Springfield ReManufacturing Company (SRC) in Springfield, Missouri is in the business of refurbishing engines, worn gears, and other components of heavy equipment to make them like new. This company is unique because of their approach to employee and managerial responsibility. According to company founder, Jack Stack, "The best, most efficient, most profitable way to operate a business is to give everybody in the company a voice in saying how the company is run and a stake in the financial outcome, good or bad."

After America's double-dip recession in the 1980s, Stack realized he had to take desperate measures to keep his business from failing. He decided to share the company's financials with every employee. Stack taught everyone, from mechanics to executives, the unspoken rules of business and challenged them to help the company move their numbers—and it made a difference! Stack began an approach to business called Open-Book Management. He decided he wanted to show employees what kind of company they were entering before they started the job, and today, every candidate from senior executive to facilities management must learn how to read and comprehend the company's financial books before they are considered for hire.

Every employee at SRC is required to habitually ask, "What could go wrong, and what are we going to do when it does?" Each employee takes responsibility for the work accomplished, their efficiency and productivity and because they know the financial impact their work will have for company numbers.

THE RESULTS

Because of the responsibility on the shoulders of its employees, Springfield ReManufacturing Corp. stock is now worth over $70 a share, compared to the $0.10 per share that it was worth in 1983. ***The company's value has increased in value by over 360,000%.***

BEST PRACTICE

DELEGA DECISI

The number of decisions a typical leader makes is staggering. The question that comes to mind is why do most leaders make so many decisions? Leaders who desire for their people to be more responsible empower them to make more decisions.

Do you remember the first time a leader delegated an important decision to you? Can you recall when a supervisor asked, "What do you think we should do?" How did you feel when you knew the outcome might be affected by your opinion? Exhilarated? Energized? Engaged? Your people can feel the same way if you will trust them.

As the leader, no one in your organization has a better view of the vision than you do. There is also a good chance you have more experience than most of those you lead. Because of these factors, the tendency to TRY to make every decision is understandable. Resist the temptation. While there are decisions that only you should make, truthfully most could be made by someone else. When you do delegate, don't allow yourself to micro-manage the person who is deciding. Really trust them and allow them to feel the weight of the outcome and then coach accordingly.

If you want to accelerate the growth of your business, decide to stop doing so much deciding. Trust your people and **DELEGATE DECISIONS**. They really do want more responsibility.

When you trust your people engagement skyrockets.

SPOTLIGHT

UNDER ARMOUR

At Under Armour, leaders avoid making unilateral decisions and go out of their way to gather input from their most trusted employees. CEO Kevin Plank always recruits employees to help make decisions, asking, "What would you do if you were in my shoes?" Plank credits his success with UA to seeking input before making decisions.

ASSESSMENT

RATE EACH STATEMENT USING THE FOLLOWING:

5	Strongly Agree	2	Disagree
4	Agree	1	Strongly Disagree
3	Neutral		

Our organization has a clear process for decision-making. ________

Everyone on our team accepts responsibility for their decisions. ________

Every employee would say decision-making is an important part of their role. ________

Employees are encouraged to weigh in on important decisions. ________

Leaders in our organization delegate decisions to the people closest to the customers. ________

Note any statements you ranked in the one to three range. How can you improve these areas? Consider Things You Can Do (p. 70) to address these development opportunities.

Great organizations empower decision makers at all levels.

TEAM TIME

REVIEW WITH YOUR TEAM:

Dedicate 10-15 minutes of your next Team Meeting to work through two to three of the following questions and activities.

THINGS TO REMEMBER

1. **GREAT ORGANIZATIONS EMPOWER DECISION MAKERS AT ALL LEVELS**
2. **WEIGH-IN LEADS TO BUY IN**
3. **WHEN YOU MAKE THE DECISION, YOU CARE MORE ABOUT THE DECISION**

INTRODUCTION: Review the BEST PRACTICE SPOTLIGHT: UNDER ARMOUR (p. 67) and share the story with your team. What are their initial reactions? Who do you currently need to delegate a decision to?

ASSESSMENT: Take a minute to work through the assessment questions (p. 68) and debrief your answers with your team.

DISCUSSION: Where have you recently observed a leader delegate a decision, and what effect did it have? How can we become an organization that trusts people to make decisions?

GROUP ACTIVITY: Review the DELEGATE DECISIONS THINGS YOU CAN DO (p. 70) with the team, break into groups of three to four, and brainstorm additional ideas—challenge each group to develop at least ten additional ideas and be prepared to report back to the team.

NEXT STEPS: Have each member of the team choose one of the ideas from the list on page 70 (or from the ideas generated during your group activity) and do it over the next week. Ask leaders to report back to the team at your next meeting.

THINGS YOU CAN DO

		DATE COMPLETED:
☐	**DECISION AUDIT** Keep a log or journal of the decisions you make in the upcoming week. The following week try to give away 10% of them. Repeat the process week after week until you identify the critical few decisions you should not delegate.	
☐	**GIVE IT AWAY** Choose a project to delegate. Refuse to micromanage or specify methods, but be clear on the desired outcomes and any boundaries that exist.	
☐	**STRETCH ASSIGNMENTS** Come up with at least three assignments (with appropriate decision-making authority) this month that will stretch a Team Member to perform at a higher level and contribute more to the company.	
☐	**WHAT'S NEXT?** When someone delivers results on an assignment, make it a habit to give them a bigger opportunity.	
☐	**CONFIRM CLARITY** Every time you delegate a big decision, follow up with written communication to ensure the expectations are clear.	
☐	**IT'S YOURS!** Look at your to-do list and give away one thing each week to a trusted coworker.	
☐	**PLAY TO THEIR STRENGTHS** Choose a task to delegate in the coming week. Identify a Team Member who has the ability to handle the task within their area of strength.	
☐	**2-D** Ask each member of your leadership team to come up with two things a month they can delegate (2-D) to another employee. Hold them accountable for developing their ability to delegate.	
☐	**DELEGATE UPDATE** Once you delegate a decision, empower and entrust the person to own it. Ask for updates as needed.	
☐	**FUEL GROWTH** At your next team meeting, remind your leaders to keep delegating responsibilities in order to help others grow.	

What else could you and other leaders do to **DELEGATE DECISIONS**?

☐		
☐		

NOTES

BEST PRACTICE

SHARE OWNER

Do you know anyone who has too much stuff? This behavior taken to the extreme leads to a disorder known as hoarding. Some leaders are hoarders and try to own more than they should. Owning every decision, outcome, and initiative is clutter and can impede capacity. High performing leaders are quick to **SHARE OWNERSHIP** and as a result, they enhance their effectiveness while developing those around them.

In the best organizations, everyone owns something and everything is owned. As you take inventory of your leadership, do you feel overwhelmed with your responsibilities? Do you have a tendency to hold on to too much or micro-manage those you lead? If you will share ownership throughout your organization, the level of engagement will improve.

Your people crave your trust, but responsibility should not be given blindly. Start small—but start! When your people take ownership of the little things, then you can trust them with greater responsibilities.

Ultimately, leaders carry the weight of responsibility for everything they lead. There is an old saying, "Two are better than one, because they have a good return for their work." High performance leaders understand the power of shared ownership, and their results flourish. The people around you are willing to help you carry the load if you are willing to share ownership. Is it time for you to de-clutter your leadership and trust your people?

Responsibility is a key driver for genuine care and engagement

SPOTLIGHT

REI

REI has created an online company campfire that allows the retailer's top managers to share ideas. The 11,000+ employees weigh in and then take ownership of implementing the agreed upon ideas. At REI, everyone is encouraged to own the ideas of the company!

ASSESSMENT

RATE EACH STATEMENT USING THE FOLLOWING:

5	Strongly Agree	2	Disagree
4	Agree	1	Strongly Disagree
3	Neutral		

Leaders in our organization empower workers and make them feel valuable. ________

Our employees are challenged to take on more responsibility. ________

We have a culture where employees are allowed to try new things and fail. ________

Our leaders have capacity and margin because of their willingness to delegate. ________

There is a sense of shared ownership throughout our organization. ________

Note any statements you ranked in the one to three range. How can you improve these areas? Consider Things You Can Do (p. 76) to address these development opportunities.

In great organizations, everyone owns something, and everything is owned.

TEAM TIME

REVIEW WITH YOUR TEAM:

Dedicate 10-15 minutes of your next Team Meeting to work through two to three of the following questions and activities.

THINGS TO REMEMBER

1. **HIGH PERFORMANCE LEADERS TRUST THEIR PEOPLE ENOUGH TO SHARE OWNERSHIP**
2. **SHARING OWNERSHIP GROWS CAPACITY AND ENGAGEMENT**
3. **IN GREAT ORGANIZATIONS, EVERYONE OWNS SOMETHING, AND EVERYTHING IS OWNED**

INTRODUCTION: Review the BEST PRACTICE SPOTLIGHT: REI (p. 73) and share the story with your team. What are their initial reactions? How well do you share ownership with those you lead?

ASSESSMENT: Take a minute to work through the assessment questions (p. 74) and debrief your answers with your team.

DISCUSSION: Where have you recently observed a leader in our organization share ownership with a direct report, and what effect did it have? How can we become an organization where leaders more effectively share ownership?

GROUP ACTIVITY: Review the SHARE OWNERSHIP THINGS YOU CAN DO (p. 76) with the team, break into groups of three to four, and brainstorm additional ideas—challenge each group to develop at least ten additional ideas and be prepared to report back to the team.

NEXT STEPS: Have each member of the team choose one of the ideas from the list on page 76 (or from the ideas generated during your group activity) and do it over the next week. Ask leaders to report back to the team at your next meeting.

THINGS YOU CAN DO

		DATE COMPLETED:
☐	**EMPOWER SOMEONE** Choose one responsibility this week to give away. Select someone you think is ready for a challenge and empower them. Check back in a week to see how things are going.	
☐	**VALUE OF REAL RESPONSIBILITY** Name a real responsibility you can assign this week that will indicate you value a Team Member's contribution to the company.	
☐	**OWNERSHIP AUDIT** Take a look at your employee roster. Beside each person's name, make a list of what they own. Does everyone own something?	
☐	**BIG ROCKS** Identify the most important factors in your success as an organization. Is there clear ownership for each of these "Big Rocks?"	
☐	**TEAM FEEDBACK** Create a formal mechanism for your team to offer feedback and input on important decisions.	
☐	**CROSS TRAINING** Review your list of staff and look for ways you can cross train them in the event they have to step in for a co-worker.	
☐	**NO SILOS ALLOWED** Review the structure of your company and make sure it is set up to work collaboratively. Eliminate the silos.	
☐	**FIGURE IT OUT** List five ways you can encourage Team Members to solve their own work-related problems.	
☐	**YOU SHOULD KEEP THIS** Be slow to accept work from a Team Member. Instead, ask questions such as, "What have you attempted already? What have you learned? What next steps could you take?"	
☐	**STOP DOING LIST** Make a list of ten activities you should eliminate.	

What else could you and other leaders do to **SHARE OWNERSHIP**?

☐		
☐		

NOTES

BEST PRACTICE

ESTABLIS ACCOUN

If you need a picture of accountability, look no further than your bathroom scales. They never lie. Those who value fitness don't view the scales as something bad. In fact, they appreciate the power of the accountability they provide. The scales are unemotional. They simply give information that reflects how a person is doing in the areas of exercise and nutrition. Unfortunately, when it comes to accountability in the workplace, people often view it as a negative thing.

As a leader, you have the opportunity to reframe accountability and establish it as a gift for your people. In high performance environments, growth is a priority, and accountability is one of the most powerful ways to spur people toward their targets.

Establishing accountability starts with a set of clear and agreed upon expectations. Once expectations are in place, leaders need to check in often to evaluate progress. There is little value in having expectations and then never talking about them. Don't wait until an annual performance review—have ongoing accountability conversations throughout the year.

Accountability can be a great motivator in a growing organization. If you want your people to take responsibility for their actions, then give them permission to make progress, and coach them along the way. There is tremendous potential in your organization. Will you give your people the gift and **ESTABLISH ACCOUNTABILITY**?

When people take ownership outcomes improve.

H
TABILITY

SPOTLIGHT

GOOGLE

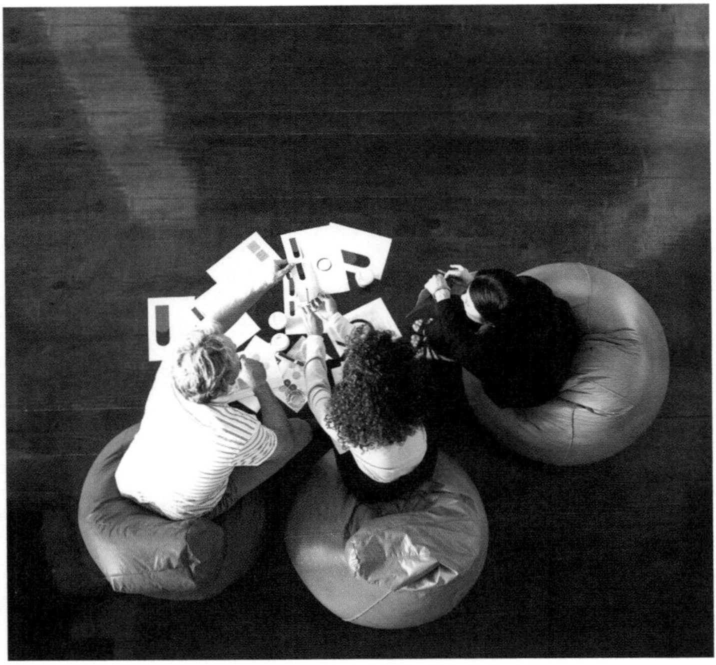

Back in 1999, when Google was less than a year old, John Doerr introduced the concept of OKRs (Objectives and Key Results). Google still uses OKRs to keep people accountable and aligned on the work that matters. Employees use "Doerr's goal formula," ... I will ________ as measured by ____________.

ASSESSMENT

RATE EACH STATEMENT USING THE FOLLOWING:

5	Strongly Agree	2	Disagree
4	Agree	1	Strongly Disagree
3	Neutral		

Clear expectations have been established for every employee. ________

Employees in our organization are held accountable for methods and outcomes. ________

Feedback is provided in a timely fashion when performance gaps are identified. ________

Everyone, from senior leaders to the front line, understands the role accountability plays in our success. ________

Our employees see accountability as a gift. ________

Note any statements you ranked in the one to three range. How can you improve these areas? Consider Things You Can Do (p. 82) to address these development opportunities.

In great organizations, accountability is viewed as a gift.

TEAM TIME

REVIEW WITH YOUR TEAM:

Dedicate 10-15 minutes of your next Team Meeting to work through two to three of the following questions and activities.

THINGS TO REMEMBER

1. **ACCOUNTABILITY IMPROVES PERFORMANCE**
2. **THE BEST LEADERS CONSISTENTLY GIVE THE GIFT OF ACCOUNTABILITY**
3. **ACCOUNTABILITY INCREASES ENGAGEMENT**

INTRODUCTION: Review the **BEST PRACTICE SPOTLIGHT: GOOGLE** (p. 79) and share the story with your team. What are their initial reactions? How well do you hold people accountable?

ASSESSMENT: Take a minute to work through the assessment questions (p. 80) and debrief your answers with your team.

DISCUSSION: Where have you recently observed a leader in our organization hold someone accountable, and what effect did it have? How can we establish accountability throughout our organization?

GROUP ACTIVITY: Review the **ESTABLISH ACCOUNTABILITY THINGS YOU CAN DO** (p. 82) with the team, break into groups of three to four, and brainstorm additional ideas—challenge each group to develop at least ten additional ideas and be prepared to report back to the team.

NEXT STEPS: Have each member of the team choose one of the ideas from the list on page 82 (or from the ideas generated during your group activity) and do it over the next week. Ask leaders to report back to the team at your next meeting.

THINGS YOU CAN DO

		DATE COMPLETED:
☐	**ONE ON ONE** Have an accountability conversation with a different employee at the first of every month for the next year. Agree upon one area where you will be accountable to each other. Report back on progress at the end of the month.	
☐	**CHECKLIST CHECKUP** Assign action items on who is going to do what by when at the end of every team meeting. At the next meeting, hold Team Members accountable for their action items.	
☐	**CLARIFY EXPECTATIONS** When discussing an assignment with your team, always recap what is expected of each individual.	
☐	**MODEL ACCOUNTABILITY** Give your team permission to hold you accountable. Choose one area of focus each week for four weeks and share with your team what you are committed to doing. Report back weekly on your progress.	
☐	**ON THE 30S** Check in with new Team Members every 30 days for at least three months to review the company mission.	
☐	**REVISIT YOUR VALUES** The next time you face a problem, examine it in light of your values and evaluate if you are being true to who you want to be.	
☐	**FEEDBACK EARLY & OFTEN** Establish a detailed review every 30 days with all new employees for their first four months.	
☐	**THE LAST 10%** In conversations with your direct reports, commit to sharing the last 10% of the truth. Remember that candid feedback can be a catalyst for growth.	
☐	**DON'T PROCRASTINATE** Ask yourself if a difficult conversation with an employee is needed concerning a poor attitude or mediocre performance. If so, talk to them openly as soon as possible.	
☐	**TRACK THE COMMITMENTS** Make sure your leadership team tracks commitments Team Members make in order to hold them accountable. Review previous action items every time you meet.	

What else could you and other leaders do to **ESTABLISH ACCOUNTABILITY**?

☐		
☐		

NOTES

RESPONSIBILITY SUMMARY

Sharing responsibility is one of the best things you can do to develop your people. High Performance Organizations are filled with people who take ownership of their role and care about the overall mission.

BEST PRACTICES REVIEW

DELEGATE DECISIONS – Growing organizations empower decision makers at all levels.

SHARE OWNERSHIP – In High Performance Organizations, everyone owns something and everything is owned.

ESTABLISH ACCOUNTABILITY – People perform better and care more when they are held accountable.

NEXT STEPS

- Do a Responsibility audit by reviewing the assessment questions on pages 68, 74, and 80 to evaluate whether the above best practices are present in your organization. Create a plan to close any gaps you discover and challenge your team to share responsibility with everyone in the company.
- Have a monthly conversation with your leadership team and identify areas where each of you can do a better job of giving responsibility to your people. Share stories of progress moving forward.
- Beginning immediately, set a personal goal of delegating a decision, a task, or a project every week for the next month. Follow up with an accountability conversation.

NOTES

The one thing I need to do to share **RESPONSIBILITY** is:

Other thoughts:

ENVIRO

SECTION FOUR

Some environments are better than others. Which do you prefer: beach, mountains, or the lake? Do you like playing outside when it's hot and sunny, or would you choose cold and snowy? We all have our preferences. Work environments are no different and play a huge role in whether people care about their jobs and stay engaged. Great leaders create an atmosphere where people can thrive.

Step one in creating the right **ENVIRONMENT** is to provide safety. When employees walk through your doors, they need to know the work conditions will be safe, positive, and worker-friendly. If people don't feel safe, not only will they refuse to be fully engaged, they will quickly begin to look for a new place to work.

Another way to provide a great environment is to equip for success. Nothing is more frustrating than being asked to do a job you are not trained to do. Great leaders create a culture of continuous improvement and ensure workers have the skills to meet the demands of their positions.

Finally, a great work environment is one where leaders listen and respond in real time. When employees show up knowing leaders care enough to listen, they care more.

As the leader, you are responsible for the environment. Work to create the kind of place you would like to work, and your people will show up every day ready to contribute their best.

The best leaders create an Environment of Connection, Affirmation, and Responsibility.

BEST PRACTICES

PROVIDE SAFETY • • **EQUIP FOR SUCCESS** • • **LISTEN & RESPOND**

CASE STUDY

"Culture" is more than a buzzword at Warby Parker (WP). This trendy eyewear brand has dedicated an entire team to promoting the company's internal community values. Selling eyewear doesn't mean boring. At Warby Parker, a fun company event or program is always on an employee's calendar. Their leadership believes in giving people something to look forward to and promoting an environment where teamwork and fun are valued. The company has been known to send random employees to lunch together in an effort to promote unity, friendship, and greater collaboration among staff.

Warby Parker has a mission statement just for culture: "Create an environment where employees can think big, have fun, and do good." WP considers customers, employees, community, and the environment as stakeholders. In an interview, co-founder David Gilboa shared the intentional strategies they use to create a coveted culture. They value onboarding, communication, and celebration, while encouraging continual learning. Gilboa believes these main values are why WP is known to be an environment of camaraderie and productivity.

Who wouldn't want to work in an environment where, every month, employees nominate a few coworkers to win prizes valued at hundreds of dollars? Plus, employees are encouraged to travel internationally to see the company's mission in action through their Buy a Pair, Give a Pair program. At Warby Parker, they treat people the way they want to be treated!

THE RESULTS

With an environment of growth, creativity, and philanthropy, no wonder Warby Parker has been honored multiple times for their innovation and won the Jefferson Award for Outstanding Service. ***Additionally, Warby Parker has donated 1 million pairs of eyeglasses to people in need.***

BEST PRACTICE

PROVIDE SAFETY

Have you ever stood on a hotel balcony overlooking the ocean enjoying the amazing view? Few would experience the joy without the presence of the balcony rail. The rail provides safety and confidence. Every day, thousands of people enter their work places without feeling safe, and their lack of confidence prevents them from being fully engaged. As the leader, your primary responsibility is to **PROVIDE SAFETY** for your people.

Like fear, safety comes in all shapes and sizes. Wise leaders start by creating a positive environment—one where people are individually affirmed and where negativity is squelched. Toxic attitudes and inappropriate behaviors are not tolerated in great organizations.

Physical safety also matters. Work conditions must allow employees to do their jobs without fear and customers to do business with confidence. Shortcuts end up costing more in the long run.

Finally, the best leaders ensure their workplace is psychologically safe. They create an atmosphere where people are allowed to speak freely and honestly without fear of consequences.

If the level of engagement in your business appears to be low, your people may not feel safe. If you will create a balcony rail of support, trust will grow and so will engagement.

When workers feel safe, trust grows.

SPOTLIGHT

ATKINS ENERGY AMERICA

At Atkins Energy America, employees are encouraged to participate in the company's Good Catch/Near Miss program. Any employee can submit an incident considered a Good Catch—something that might have caused an accident if gone unnoticed, or a Near Miss—anything with the potential to cause an accident.

ASSESSMENT

RATE EACH STATEMENT USING THE FOLLOWING:

5	Strongly Agree	2	Disagree
4	Agree	1	Strongly Disagree
3	Neutral		

Employees in our organization feel physically safe at work. ________

Our workplace is healthy and vibrant. ________

Our workers freely share ideas for improvement and constructive feedback. ________

When disagreements arise, our Team Members work together for resolution. ________

Our employees protect each other and the culture of our organization. ________

Note any statements you ranked in the one to three range. How can you improve these areas? Consider Things You Can Do (p. 96) to address these development opportunities.

Trust grows when people feel safe.

TEAM TIME

REVIEW WITH YOUR TEAM:

Dedicate 10-15 minutes of your next Team Meeting to work through two to three of the following questions and activities.

THINGS TO REMEMBER

1. **FEAR COMES IN ALL SHAPES AND SIZES**
2. **THE BEST LEADERS CREATE PSYCHOLOGICAL, CULTURAL, AND PHYSICAL SAFETY FOR THEIR PEOPLE**
3. **ENGAGEMENT GROWS WHEN PEOPLE FEEL SAFE**

INTRODUCTION: Review the **BEST PRACTICE SPOTLIGHT: ATKINS ENERGY AMERICA** (p. 93) and share the story with your team. What are their initial reactions? How well do you provide a safe environment for your people?

ASSESSMENT: Take a minute to work through the assessment questions (p. 94) and debrief your answers with your team.

DISCUSSION: Where have you recently observed someone in our organization follow a safety procedure, and what effect did it have? How can we create a safer workplace for our workers?

GROUP ACTIVITY: Review the **PROVIDE SAFETY THINGS YOU CAN DO** (p. 96) with the team, break into groups of three to four, and brainstorm additional ideas—challenge each group to develop at least ten additional ideas and be prepared to report back to the team.

NEXT STEPS: Have each member of the team choose one of the ideas from the list on page 96 (or from the ideas generated during your group activity) and do it over the next week. Ask leaders to report back to the team at your next meeting.

THINGS YOU CAN DO

		DATE COMPLETED:
☐	**SYSTEMS REVIEW** Conduct a full review of the systems within your organization to evaluate whether they are enabling or inhibiting employee safety.	
☐	**WHAT'S YOUR QUESTION?** Conduct regularly scheduled town hall style meetings with your senior leaders. Don't screen the questions in advance.	
☐	**SAFETY FOR EVERYONE** Work with your team to identify ten ways Team Members can hold one another accountable for workplace safety. Quickly implement the best ideas.	
☐	**FAIL FORWARD** At least once a week, encourage risk taking and celebrate failures. If you aren't failing at something, you're not taking enough risks.	
☐	**LEAD WITH HUMILITY** Be vulnerable and willing to admit mistakes to your team. When appropriate, ask for feedback on how you can improve.	
☐	**SEE SOMETHING & SAY SOMETHING** Ask all staff members to say something if they see something that concerns them from a safety perspective.	
☐	**PROTECT THE CULTURE** Ensure you have a written policy in place that states harassment of any kind is not permitted, and always offer a clear line of communication to report it.	
☐	**C&O ENVIRONMENT** Evaluate your environment to ensure it is C&O (clean and organized.) What needs to be changed? Create a detailed list to improve.	
☐	**CULTURE COUNCIL** Select employees from all levels and several departments to sit on a Culture Council. Their charge: Identify the attributes of the culture to be leveraged and those that need to change to create a more vibrant place to work.	
☐	**GUARD THE TEAM** Evaluate the cultural norms in place to protect your team. Ask yourself: are they clear and well-communicated, and is anything missing?	

What else could you and other leaders do to **PROVIDE SAFETY**?

☐		
☐		

NOTES

BEST PRACTICE

EQUIP FOR SU

The right tools can make a hard task not only doable but enjoyable. Have you ever attempted a do-it-yourself project when you didn't have the correct tools? Frustrating—to say the least! One of the ways you can create a better environment for your people is to equip them for success.

Successful organizations are typically filled with workers who are growing in their abilities and are prepared to take on more responsibility. Do you have a profile for what each Team Member needs to be able to do to master each role? Once you have the profile in place, train on the basics. Your environment needs to be one where workers are so skilled, performance becomes second nature.

The best environments encourage people to master the skills for their current job but also prepare them for future opportunities. Skills don't need to be limited to a single role or responsibility. If you truly want your people to be successful, teach them broader skills such as how to resolve conflict, solve problems, and manage change.

Don't ask people to do a job they are not prepared to do. Make it a habit to **EQUIP FOR SUCCESS**. Your employee will not only enjoy the work, they will do a better job today and be prepared for tomorrow.

When leaders invest in their people today they ensure a better tomorrow.

SPOTLIGHT

THE CONTAINER STORE

The Container Store is committed to equipping their people. Before they ever put an employee in front of a customer, they require 40 hours of training. But it doesn't stop there. Full time employees eventually receive almost 300 hours of paid training during the first year!

ASSESSMENT

RATE EACH STATEMENT USING THE FOLLOWING:

5 Strongly Agree
4 Agree
3 Neutral
2 Disagree
1 Strongly Disagree

Every employee has a clear, agreed-upon definition of success. __________

Our people are trained and equipped to meet the expectations of their role. __________

Everyone on our payroll is expected to grow. __________

Our organization budgets resources to provide growth opportunities for employees. __________

Team Members are equipped with the skills they need to be successful. __________

Note any statements you ranked in the one to three range. How can you improve these areas? Consider Things You Can Do (p. 102) to address these development opportunities.

In the best organizations, people are equipped to win!

TEAM TIME

REVIEW WITH YOUR TEAM:

Dedicate 10-15 minutes of your next Team Meeting to work through two to three of the following questions and activities.

THINGS TO REMEMBER

1. **WITHOUT THE PROPER SKILLS, WORK BECOMES DRUDGERY**
2. **EVERYONE DESERVES CLEAR EXPECTATIONS**
3. **WITHOUT THE REQUISITE TRAINING, HIGH LEVELS OF ENGAGEMENT ARE IMPOSSIBLE**

INTRODUCTION: Review the **BEST PRACTICE SPOTLIGHT: THE CONTAINER STORE** (p. 99) and share the story with your team. What are their initial reactions? How well do you equip people for success?

ASSESSMENT: Take a minute to work through the assessment questions (p. 100) and debrief your answers with your team.

DISCUSSION: Where have you recently observed a leader in our organization equip others for success, and what effect did it have? Where do we need to do a better job of training our people?

GROUP ACTIVITY: Review the **EQUIP FOR SUCCESS THINGS YOU CAN DO** (p. 102) with the team, break into groups of three to four, and brainstorm additional ideas—challenge each group to develop at least ten additional ideas and be prepared to report back to the team.

NEXT STEPS: Have each member of the team choose one of the ideas from the list on page 102 (or from the ideas generated during your group activity) and do it over the next week. Ask leaders to report back to the team at your next meeting.

THINGS YOU CAN DO

		DATE COMPLETED:
☐	**DEVELOPMENT PLAN** Ensure all Team Members have a development plan in place that clearly identifies areas of targeted growth.	
☐	**BASIC TRAINING** Provide every employee with basic training for their current role.	
☐	**TRAINING BUDDY** Assign a training buddy to each new employee. Ask the veteran to support the new hire until fully trained for current position.	
☐	**SUCCESS RESOURCES** Send a list to your team of all resources and leadership development opportunities your organization provides to support their growth.	
☐	**THE STANDARDS** In order for your company to reach its full potential and your people to be fully engaged, everyone must know what is expected of them. Meet with every Team Member in the next 30 days to clarify the standards for each role they fill.	
☐	**INSPIRATION** Offer at least one inspirational story or quote every week to help your team focus on what matters most.	
☐	**SUPPORT SYSTEM** Communicate to your leadership team the necessity of offering as much support as possible to their teams in order to ensure success.	
☐	**SKILL GAPS** Work with each Team Member individually to identify any skill gaps that need to be addressed. Create a plan and get started.	
☐	**ATTITUDE MATTERS** Examine your attitude at work and list ways you can be more positive. Share your list with your leadership team, and remind them that a positive attitude will help everyone win.	
☐	**READING ON LEADING** Pick an area of leadership needed for your team to improve. Choose a book that addresses this topic and provide a copy to each member of your team. Read the book together and discuss what you are learning. Create a plan for improvement and act on the plan.	

What else could you and other leaders do to **EQUIP FOR SUCCESS**?

☐		
☐		

NOTES

BEST PRACTICE

LISTEN & RESP

Are you a good listener? There aren't many things better than being heard. If you **LISTEN AND RESPOND** to your employees, your environment moves from good to great.

The ability to listen well is a skill. How much do you work on it? The best leaders learn when to speak and when to stay silent. Unfortunately, too many leaders react rather than respond. They assume being in charge makes them smarter; listening makes you smarter and helps you make better decisions.

Do you spend time listening to your frontline employees? They are a real-time market survey to what your customers are experiencing and to their level of satisfaction. The people closest to your customers are closest to your problems and the solutions.

If you really want to create a great environment for those you lead, make sure you build in time to listen to your people and respond quickly and appropriately. A culture where leaders listen and respond is a culture where everyone cares more.

Real conversations are the bridge to real connections.

SPOTLIGHT

TOYOTA

In 1951, Toyota created a feedback system for employees to share ideas on how to increase productivity. Virtually no idea was considered too small or insignificant. Forty years into their journey, they had received over 20 million ideas! Now, they receive over 700,000 ideas a year. These suggestions result in tens of millions of dollars in cost savings and increased productivity.

ASSESSMENT

RATE EACH STATEMENT USING THE FOLLOWING:

5 Strongly Agree
4 Agree
3 Neutral
2 Disagree
1 Strongly Disagree

Our leaders proactively seek feedback from employees. ________

Employees know their voice will be heard. ________

Feedback and input are processed and responded to in a timely fashion. ________

Front line Team Members are encouraged to weigh in on important decisions.________

Everyone in the organization has the opportunity to give annual feedback. ________

Note any statements you ranked in the one to three range. How can you improve these areas? Consider Things You Can Do (p. 108) to address these development opportunities.

The people closest to the problem are closest to the solution.

TEAM TIME

REVIEW WITH YOUR TEAM:

Dedicate 10-15 minutes of your next Team Meeting to work through two to three of the following questions and activities.

THINGS TO REMEMBER

1. **LISTENING COMMUNICATES CARE**
2. **THE PEOPLE CLOSEST TO THE PROBLEM ARE CLOSEST TO THE SOLUTION**
3. **WISE LEADERS SEEK INPUT, THEN RESPOND QUICKLY**

INTRODUCTION: Review the **BEST PRACTICE SPOTLIGHT: TOYOTA** (p. 105) and share the story with your team. What are their initial reactions? How well do you listen to your people and respond to their input?

ASSESSMENT: Take a minute to work through the assessment questions (p. 106) and debrief your answers with your team.

DISCUSSION: Where have you recently observed a leader in our organization listen and respond toward a teammate, and what effect did it have? How can we improve the way we listen and respond to our employees?

GROUP ACTIVITY: Review the **LISTEN AND RESPOND THINGS YOU CAN DO** (p. 108) with the team, break into groups of three to four, and brainstorm additional ideas—challenge each group to develop at least ten additional ideas and be prepared to report back to the team.

NEXT STEPS: Have each member of the team choose one of the ideas from the list on page 108 (or from the ideas generated during your group activity) and do it over the next week. Ask leaders to report back to the team at your next meeting.

THINGS YOU CAN DO

		DATE COMPLETED:
☐	**STOP, LOOK, LISTEN, RESPOND** When a Team Member shares a concern, stop what you are doing, look at them, listen to them, and respond as needed.	
☐	**BAD APPLES** If you consistently hear of an employee bringing the team down, consider a replacement. Review your team quarterly to ensure everyone is still an asset to the organization.	
☐	**MONITOR MORALE** Survey your employees to monitor morale. Make improvements based on their feedback.	
☐	**FOLLOW YOUR HEART** Be sure your leaders understand the impact an employee's personal problems can have on the team. When you discover such an issue, show empathy and do what you can to help.	
☐	**IT STARTS AT THE TOP** Offer your Team Members the opportunity to schedule an appointment with you. Always listen first and then respond accordingly.	
☐	**ALL LEVEL LISTENING** Communicate with your team as often as possible the importance of listening at all levels.	
☐	**SHOW THEM YOU CARE** Every time you have a personal conversation with a Team Member, show you care by listening and responding.	
☐	**CONFIDENTIAL HOTLINE** Set up a hotline for employees to use to report issues in the workplace. Respond quickly and appropriately to concerns.	
☐	**READ BETWEEN THE LINES** When listening to employees, make it a habit to observe body language. If you sense something is wrong, ask how you might help.	
☐	**DON'T INTERRUPT** Work on creating the habit of not interrupting in all of your conversations. Jot a checkmark on a piece of paper every time you do. Make zero interruptions your daily goal.	

What else could you and other leaders do to **LISTEN & RESPOND**?

☐		
☐		

NOTES

ENVIRONMENT SUMMARY

Environment plays a major role in the engagement level of an employee. A safe, positive, responsive atmosphere facilitates care. If you are the leader, you are in charge of the environment. Work to create the kind of place you would like to work, and your people will thrive.

BEST PRACTICES REVIEW

PROVIDE SAFETY – The best environments are both physically and psychologically safe.

EQUIP FOR SUCCESS – The responsibility of the organization is to provide the tools, resources, and training people need to win.

LISTEN AND RESPOND – The best leaders listen to their people and respond quickly.

NEXT STEPS

- Do an Environment audit by reviewing the assessment questions on pages 94, 100, and 106 to evaluate whether the above best practices are present in your organization. Create a plan to close any gaps you discover, and challenge your team to share responsibility with everyone in the company.
- Each month have a conversation with a member of your leadership team and identify an area where the work environment could improve. Together, outline three action steps and a timeline to address the area you discussed.
- Beginning immediately, set a personal goal of having a conversation with a frontline employee every week. Make it a practice to listen 75% of the time. (e.g. If you have a 20 minute conversation, spend 15 minutes listening and 5 minutes responding.)

NOTES

The one thing I need to do to create a great **ENVIRONMENT** is:

Other thoughts:

NEXT STEPS

Congratulations on making it this far! You are serious about creating a great place to work—a place where people care about their work, their co-workers, and the organization. I hope you realize by now, it is possible!

If you worked through the Things You Can Do sections provided in each chapter, you are well on your way to raising the level of care in your organization. If you haven't begun putting those ideas into practice, we would suggest you go back through each chapter with your leaders and try some of the suggestions—you'll quickly realize they work!

Also, if you haven't done so, we recommend you read the book, **WIN THE HEART**. It will provide additional context and illustrations which may prove helpful as you implement the ideas from this Field Guide.

Two final suggestions:

BE CLEAR. Leaders set the tone, expectations, and the vision for their organizations. Help everyone understand: no matter the past, going forward, you will build on the cornerstones of CARE.

BE PATIENT. Your current culture wasn't created in a few weeks—transformation will take some time. But as long as you persist and don't give in to the ways of the past, you can raise the engagement of your entire organization.

If you need coaching along the way, Randy and his team at InteGREAT will be glad to help. You can reach them at **INFO@INTEGREATLEADERSHIP.COM**.

Enjoy the journey!

ABOUT THE AU

MARK MILLER

Mark Miller is a best-selling author, business leader, and communicator.

Mark began his Chick-fil-A career working as an hourly Team Member in 1977. In 1978, he joined the corporate staff working in the warehouse and mailroom. Since that time, he has provided leadership for Corporate Communications, Field Operations, Quality and Customer Satisfaction, Training and Development, and Leadership Development. During his tenure with Chick-fil-A, the company has grown from 75 to over 2,300 Restaurants with annual sales approaching $10 billion.

Mark began writing almost twenty years ago when he teamed up with Ken Blanchard, co-author of *The One Minute Manager*, to write *The Secret: What Great Leaders Know and Do*. *Win the Heart* is his seventh. With over 1,000,000 books in print in more than 25 languages, Mark's global impact continues to grow.

In addition to his writing, Mark enjoys speaking to leaders. Over the years, he's traveled to dozens of countries teaching for numerous international organizations. His theme is always the same: encouraging and equipping leaders!

Mark lives an active lifestyle. As a photographer, he enjoys shooting in some of the world's hardest-to-reach places such as Antarctica, Everest Base Camp, the jungles of Rwanda, and the Galapagos Islands.

Married to Donna, his high school sweetheart, for over 35 years, Mark has two sons, Justin and David, a daughter-in-law, Lindsay, and two amazing grandchildren, Addie and Logan!

Connect with Mark on Twitter @LeadersServe.

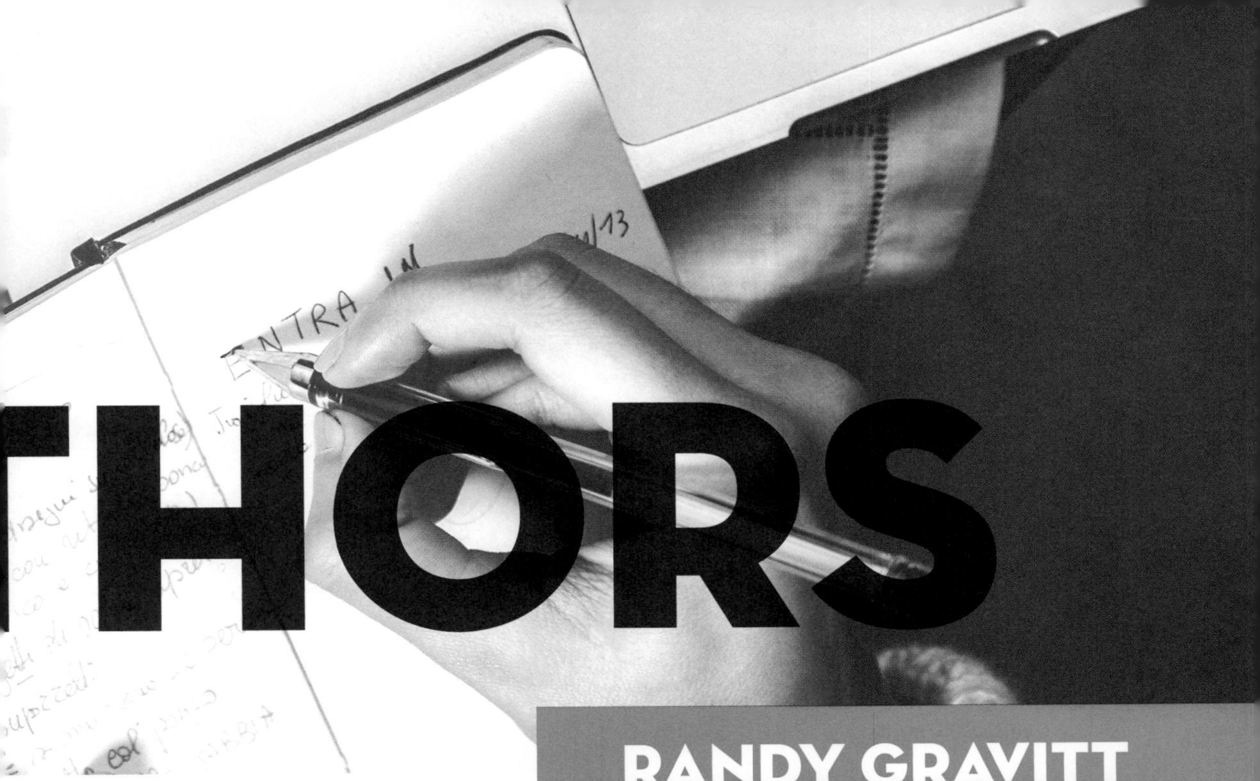

THORS

RANDY GRAVITT

Randy Gravitt is an author, speaker, and executive coach who encourages leaders to reach their potential.

Randy began his career working in education, both as a teacher and coach, before moving to Georgia where he served for nearly two decades at one of the largest churches in the Atlanta area. In 2014, Randy founded InteGREAT Leadership where he currently serves as the CEO leading a team of coaches and consultants who work with high-performance leaders, organizations, and teams all over the world.

As a speaker, Randy delivers keynotes and training workshops on the topics of leadership, team building, organizational effectiveness, and peak performance. His clients include Chick-fil-A, Grand Hyatt, Fellowship of Christian Athletes, Kroger, and the Winshape Foundation. He has also served as one of the leadership coaches for the Pittsburgh Pirates MLB Organization since 2013.

Randy's writing includes two books he has co-authored with Dan Webster, *Finding Your Way* and *Unstuck*. Both titles are aimed at helping leaders discover their passion and live fully engaged lives. Randy's desire is to serve the next generation, teaching them to understand the importance of living a life of integrity. To help leaders grow, Randy created the InteGREAT Leadership app, used by thousands daily.

In his free time, Randy enjoys playing golf, reading, fishing, and traveling. He and his wife, Laura, live in Sharpsburg, Georgia. They have four daughters, Hannah, Sarah, Rebekah, and Katherine, and two sons-in-law, Bryan and Alex. You can find Randy on social media @randygravitt or at randygravitt.com.

ADDITIONAL RESOURCES

TALENT MAGNET

HOW TO ATTRACT AND KEEP THE BEST PEOPLE

There is a long-standing truth in the world of organizations: talent wins! But how do you attract the best people? What do they really want? Based on his rigorous and extensive research, Mark Miller learned that top performers are looking for very different things than solid contributors.

Miller identifies three critical aspects of a true Talent Magnet and explores the deeper meaning of each. He pulls back the curtain on what leaders can do to find and retain the very best people--a strategic need every leader faces.

TALENT MAGNET

QUICK START GUIDE

Is it possible to accelerate the process of becoming a place that attracts Top Talent? Yes! The *Talent Magnet Quick Start Guide* is a pocket-sized tool to teach your team the three things high performers seek and is loaded with ideas to help you create a magnetic culture. Pick up a copy for each of your leaders, and begin your quest to becoming a Talent Magnet.

LEADERS MADE HERE

BUILDING A LEADERSHIP CULTURE

Great leaders create great organizations. However, a scarcity of leaders today means a shortfall in performance tomorrow. Don't gamble with your company's future!

You don't need to hope leaders emerge from the ranks or search firms can find the leaders you need in a timely fashion. Hope is not a strategy! You can build an organizational culture that will ensure your leadership pipeline is full and flowing. *Leaders Made Here* outlines a clear and replicable approach to creating the leadership bench every organization needs.

BY RANDY GRAVITT & DAN WEBSTER

FINDING YOUR WAY

DISCOVERING THE TRUTH ABOUT YOU

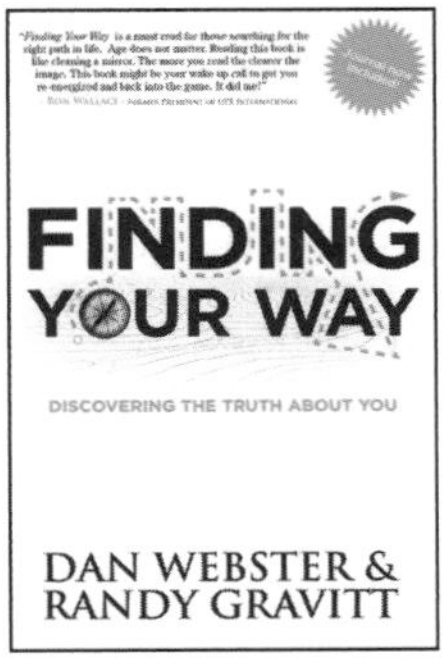

Mark Johnson is in the middle of his senior year in college and on the verge of making life-altering decisions about his future. He senses he is on the wrong path but has no way of knowing for sure. In steps 'wisdom personified' in the form of barista, Jim Clarke. Jim takes Mark under his wing and teaches him a process for discovering what career path he should take.

If you have ever wondered if you are on the right road in your own journey, *Finding Your Way* is the tool you need. Through this true-to-life fable, you will see there is a piece of Mark Johnson in all of us. Unfortunately, many go through life and never discover the truth about what they were born to do. The same doesn't have to be true for you, your friends, and those you lead.

The hardcover also includes a companion journal to guide you through the process of discovery. Visit **RANDYGRAVITT.COM** to purchase your copies of *Finding Your Way*.

UNSTUCK

A STORY ABOUT GAINING PERSPECTIVE, CREATING TRACTION, AND PURSUING YOUR PASSION

Do you feel disengaged from a life that looks good on paper? Do you wonder if there is something missing? *Unstuck: A Story about Gaining Perspective, Creating Traction, and Pursuing Your Passion* is your guide to breaking free of your comfortable cocoon and discovering what you are meant to be. Through the story of George Johnson, a man now complacent with what was once his dream job, you can learn how to shed the boredom, emptiness, and confusion and get on with your life. Whether you need a complete overhaul or just a jumpstart, you'll find the direction you need in *Unstuck*.

INTEGREAT APP

The InteGREAT Leadership app is a mobile experience designed to help leaders grow in four areas – lead self, lead others, lead teams, and lead organizations. Each bite-sized lesson is loaded with videos, assessments, and interactive experiences. The app allows you to become certified in all four areas. If you are looking for an intentional process to grow your leadership skills or leadership culture, download the InteGREAT Leadership app today.

ADDITIONAL RESOURCES

CHESS NOT CHECKERS

ELEVATE YOUR LEADERSHIP GAME

As a first time CEO, Blake Brown finds himself in over his head in a struggling organization. When he turns to his mentor, Debbie Brewster, for help, she sends him to Jack Deluca. Not only is Jack a former successful CEO, he is also a grand master chess player. Using chess as an analogy, Jack teaches Blake the four moves High Performance Organizations use to gain a competitive advantage.

The book will challenge your organization to think differently and position you to win.

CHESS NOT CHECKERS

FIELD GUIDE

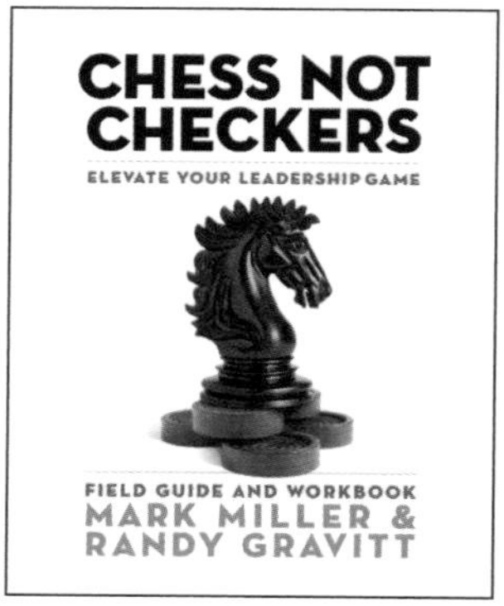

As organizations grow, the demands on leadership change. The same old moves won't cut it any more. The *Chess Not Checkers Field Guide*, a companion to the book, is a hands-on manual providing the insight and guidance to turn your company into a High Performance Organization and ensure you are thinking and acting strategically.

CHESS NOT CHECKERS

ORGANIZATIONAL ASSESSMENT

If you want to create a High Performance Organization, which of the four moves should you focus on first? Are there gaps between leadership's perception of reality and the point of view of your front-line workers? Where are your blind spots?

The *Chess Not Checkers* Organizational Assessment has been created to help you find the answers to these questions.

To get started, visit **INTEGREATLEADERSHIP.COM.**

CHESS NOT CHECKERS

VIDEO SERIES

Join your host, Randy Gravitt, on a guided tour to explore the four moves Blake learned from Jack in *Chess Not Checkers*.

Randy takes you through the content of the *Chess Not Checkers Field Guide* chapter by chapter. (The videos were produced so you can use them without the Field Guide.) This series contains more than a dozen sessions full of practical examples and group exercises.

You can purchase these at **INTEGREATLEADERSHIP.COM.**

THE SECRET

WHAT GREAT LEADERS KNOW AND DO 10TH ANNIVERSARY EDITION

International Bestseller - Over 600,000 copies sold in more than 25 languages! Join Debbie Brewster as she explores a profound yet seemingly contradictory concept: to lead is to serve. Along the way, she learns why great leaders seem preoccupied with the future, what three arenas require continuous improvement, the two essential components to leadership success, and how to knowingly strengthen her leadership credibility.

THE SECRET

FIELD GUIDE

The Secret Field Guide is a companion to the book, *The Secret What Great Leaders Know and Do*. In this practical manual, you will learn the five fundamental skills and fifteen best practices every leader needs to lead others to reach their potential.

ADDITIONAL RESOURCES

THE SECRET OF TEAMS

WHAT GREAT TEAMS KNOW AND DO

What separates teams that really deliver from the ones that simply spin their wheels? In this book, executive Debbie Brewster learns from three very different teams—the Special Forces, NASCAR, and a local restaurant. Debbie and her team discover the three elements all High Performance Teams have in common, how to change entrenched ways of thinking and acting, how to measure your progress and more.

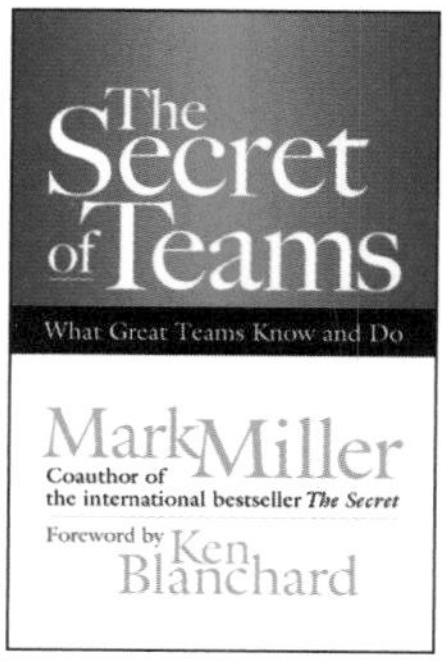

THE SECRET OF TEAMS

FIELD GUIDE

The Secret of Teams Field Guide is a how-to manual offering the 10 Best Practices of High Performance Teams. This companion resource to *The Secret of Teams* book will help you put theory into practice. If you desire to lead your people to greater results, visit **INTEGREATLEADERSHIP.COM** and purchase copies for your team today.

THE SECRET OF TEAMS

VIDEO SERIES

What is the secret to high performance?...It comes down to practicing a set of behaviors. In *The Secret of Teams* Video Series, Randy Gravitt will coach your team to build those behaviors into your culture. This resource contains 14 video sessions designed to help your team reach its potential and maximize results. You can purchase the series at **INTEGREATLEADERSHIP.COM.**

THE HEART OF LEADERSHIP

BECOMING A LEADER PEOPLE WANT TO FOLLOW

In this enlightening and entertaining business fable, Mark Miller identifies the five unique character traits exhibited by exceptional leaders. When Blake Brown is passed over for a promotion, he is sent on a quest to meet with five of his late father's colleagues, each of whom holds a piece of the leadership puzzle. This book shows us that leadership needn't be the purview of the few—it is within reach for millions around the world.

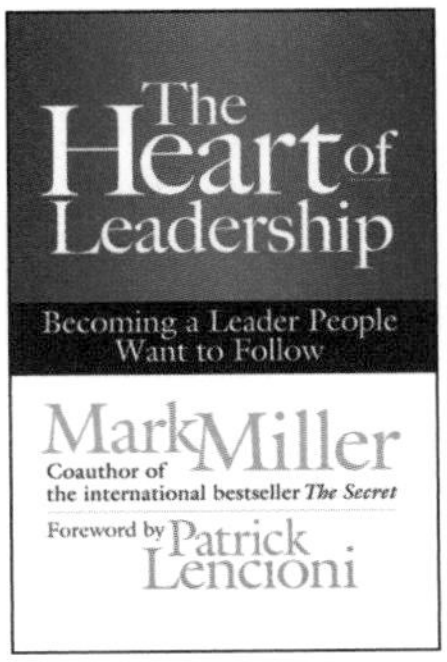

THE HEART OF LEADERSHIP

FIELD GUIDE

While leadership skills are vital, they pale in comparison to a leader's character. We all know skills can be learned, but how does a leader develop character? In *The Heart of Leadership Field Guide* you will be given the opportunity to cultivate the thing that matters most to your leadership effectiveness...YOUR Heart. This resource will challenge you to become a leader others want to follow. To purchase your copy, go to **INTEGREATLEADERSHIP.COM.**

GREAT LEADERS GROW

BECOMING A LEADER FOR LIFE

What is the key ingredient for a long-term, high-impact career in leadership? Debbie Brewster tells Blake Brown, her late mentor's son, "Your capacity to grow determines your capacity to lead," and helps Blake discover and apply four strategies for personal growth. These same strategies can enhance your life and leadership also! Join Blake and explore the path to increased leadership effectiveness and influence.

INTEGREATLEADERSHIP.COM